CONTENTS

Angels From The Realms Of Glory

Music: Traditional French. Words by James Montgomery

EASY CAROLS FOR PIANO

Chester Music
part of The Music Sales Group

London/New York/Paris/Sydney/Copenhagen/Berlin/Madrid/Tokyo

Published by
Chester Music Limited
14-15 Berners Street, London W1T 3LJ, UK.

Exclusive Distributors:
Music Sales Limited
Distribution Centre, Newmarket Road, Bury St. Edmunds, Suffolk IP33 3YB, UK.
Music Sales Corporation
257 Park Avenue South, New York, NY10010, United States of America.
Music Sales Pty Limited
120 Rothschild Avenue, Rosebery, NSW 2018, Australia.

Order No. CH66913
ISBN 1-84449-077-7
This book © Copyright 2003 by Chester Music.

Compiled and edited by Heather Ramage.
Music arranged and processed by Jerry Lanning.
Cover designed by Butterworh Design.
Printed in the United Kingdom by Printwise Limited.

Your Guarantee of Quality
As publishers, we strive to produce every book to the highest commercial standards.
The music has been freshly engraved and the book has been carefully designed to minimise
awkward page turns and to make playing from it a real pleasure.
Particular care has been given to specifying acid-free, neutral-sized paper made from pulps
which have not been elemental chlorine bleached. This pulp is from farmed sustainable
forests and was produced with special regard for the environment.
Throughout, the printing and binding have been planned to ensure a sturdy, attractive
publication which should give years of enjoyment.
If your copy fails to meet our high standards, please inform us and we will gladly replace it.

www.musicsales.com

Away In A Manger

Words & Music by William James Kirkpatrick

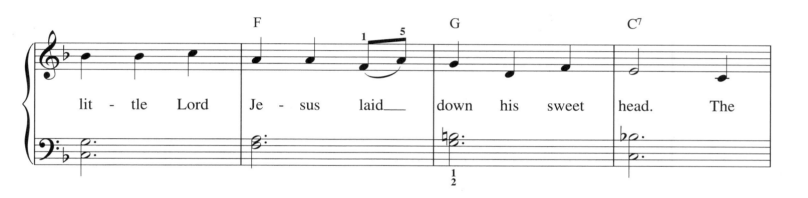

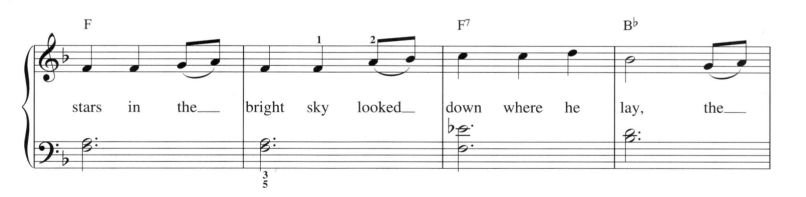

Coventry Carol

Traditional

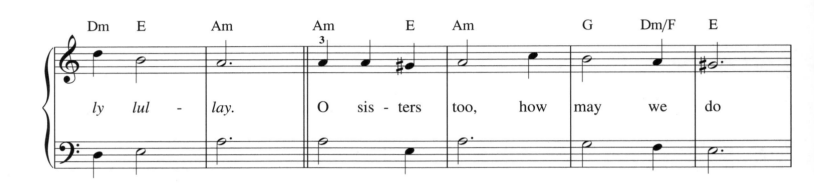

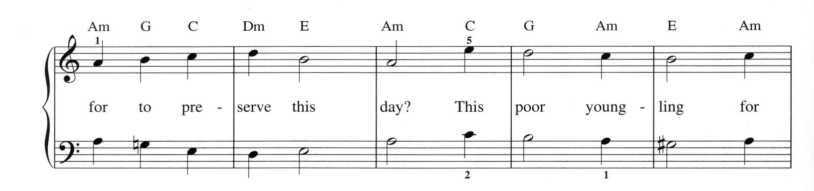

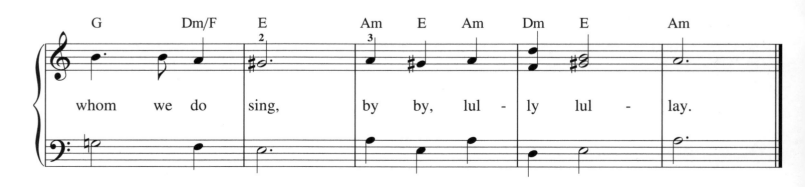

Deck The Hall

Traditional Welsh

Brightly

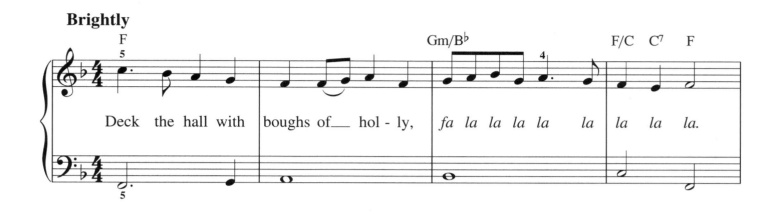

Deck the hall with boughs of__ hol - ly, *fa la la la la   la   la   la la la.*

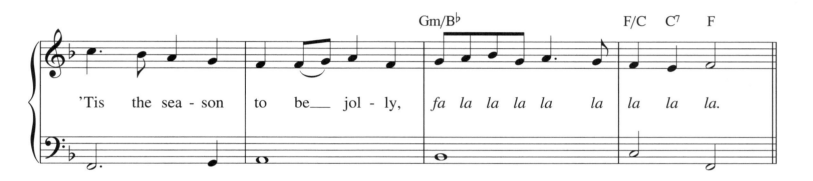

'Tis   the sea - son   to be__ jol - ly, *fa la la la la   la   la   la la.*

Fill   the mead cup,   drain   the bar - rel, *fa la la   la la la   la   la   la.*

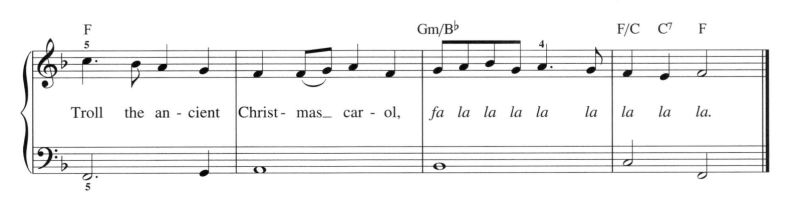

Troll   the an - cient   Christ - mas__ car - ol, *fa la la la la   la   la   la la.*

Ding Dong! Merrily On High

Music: Traditional French. Words by George Ratcliffe Woodward

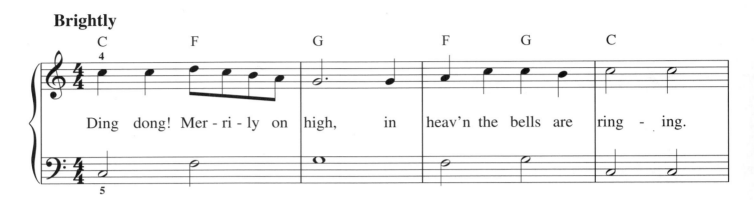

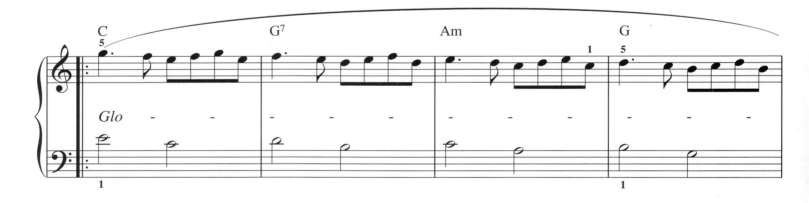

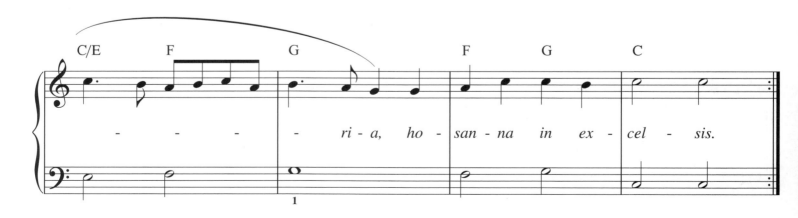

The First Nowell

Traditional

God Rest You Merry, Gentlemen

Traditional

Good King Wenceslas

Music: Traditional. Words by J.M. Neale

Quite briskly

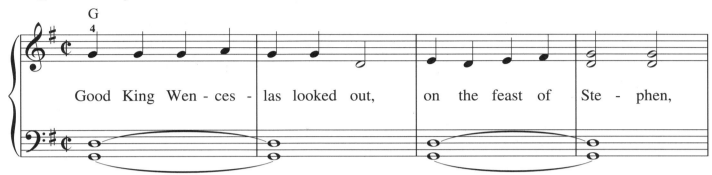

Good King Wen - ces - las looked out, on the feast of Ste - phen,

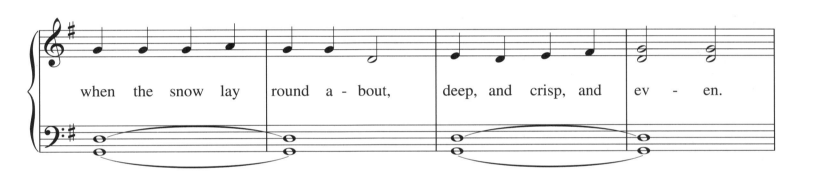

when the snow lay round a - bout, deep, and crisp, and ev - en.

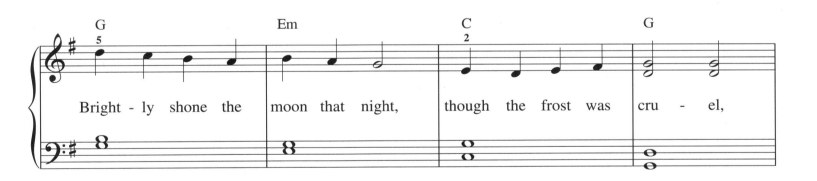

Bright - ly shone the moon that night, though the frost was cru - el,

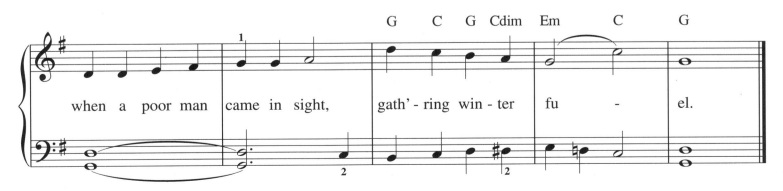

when a poor man came in sight, gath' - ring win - ter fu - el.

Hark! The Herald Angels Sing

Music by Felix Mendelssohn. Words by Charles Wesley

Here We Come A-Wassailing

Traditional

With movement

The Holly And The Ivy

Traditional

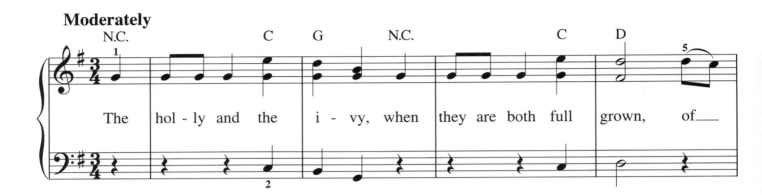

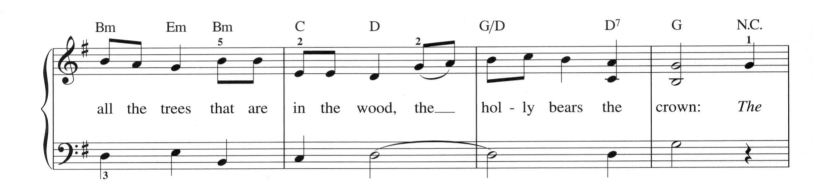

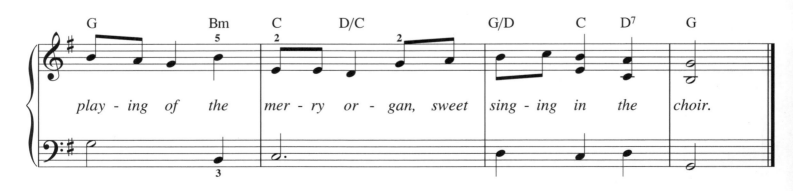

In Dulci Jubilo

Traditional. English Words by R.L. Pearsall

Moderately, with a bounce

It Came Upon The Midnight Clear

Music by Richard Storrs Willis. Words by Edmund Hamilton Sears

It__ came up - on the__ mid - night clear, that glo - rious song_ of

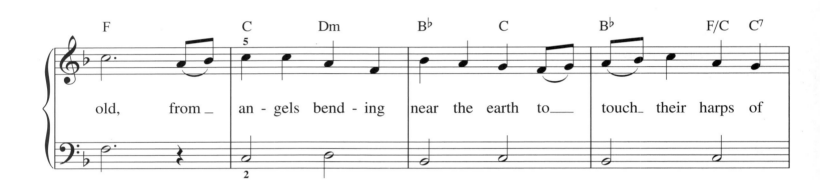

old, from _ an - gels bend - ing near the earth to__ touch_ their harps of

gold: "Peace on the earth, good - will to men, from heav'n's all gra - cious

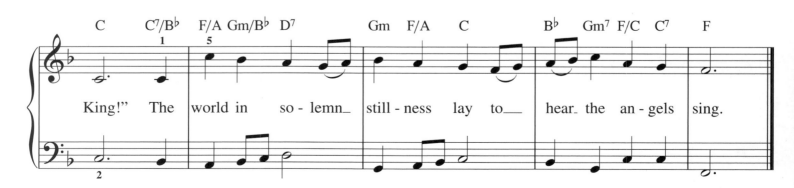

King!" The world in so - lemn_ still - ness lay to__ hear_ the an - gels sing.

Jolly Old St Nicholas

Words & Music by Vaughn Horton

Jingle Bells

Words & Music by J.S. Pierpont

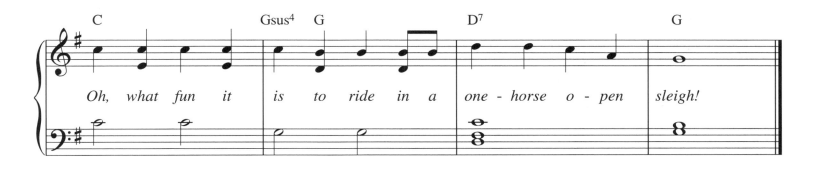

Joy To The World

Music by George Frideric Handel. Words by Isaac Watts

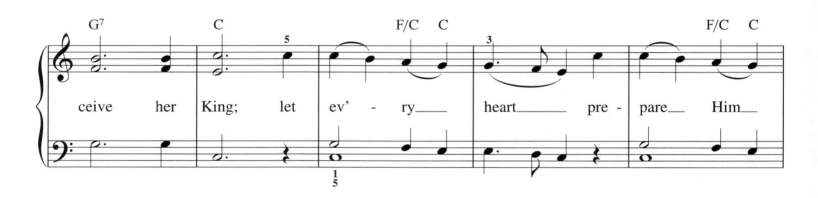

O Christmas Tree (O Tannenbaum)

Traditional

Moderately

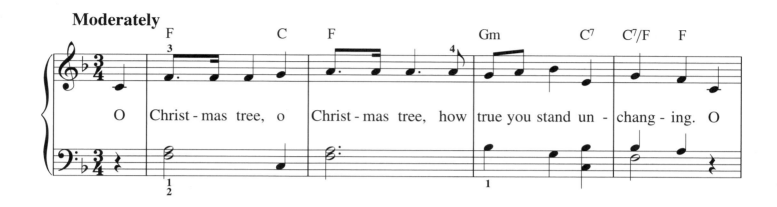

O Christ - mas tree, o Christ - mas tree, how true you stand un - chang - ing. O

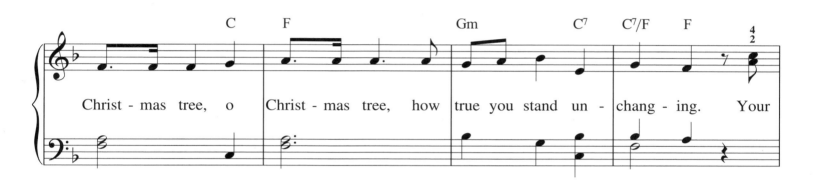

Christ - mas tree, o Christ - mas tree, how true you stand un - chang - ing. Your

boughs so green in sum - mer - time, re - main so green in win - ter - time. O

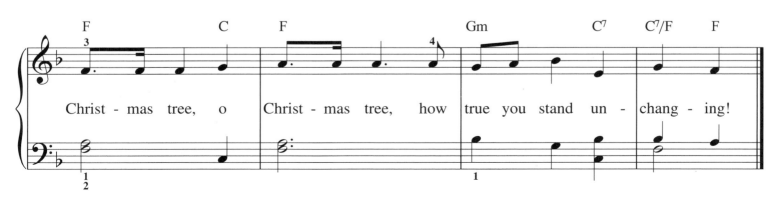

Christ - mas tree, o Christ - mas tree, how true you stand un - chang - ing!

O Come All Ye Faithful

Original Words & Music by John Francis Wade. English Words by Frederick Oakeley

O Come, O Come, Emmanuel

Traditional. English Words by John Neale

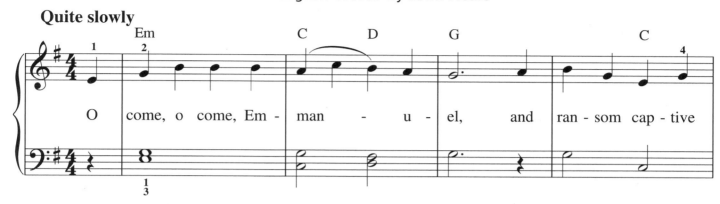

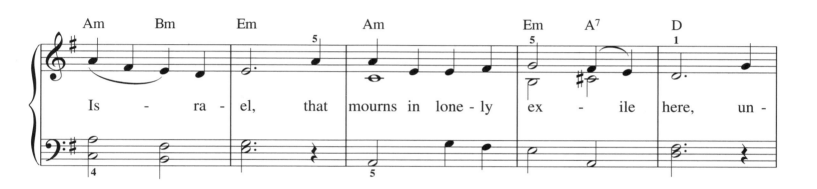

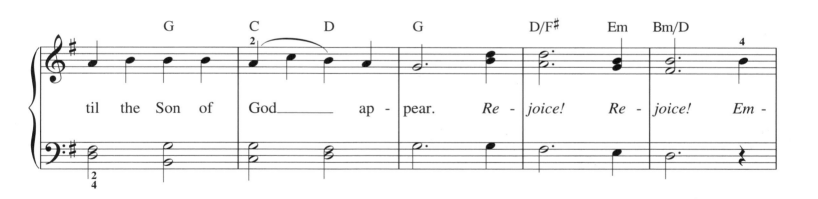

O Holy Night

By A. Adam

O Little Town Of Bethlehem

Music by Lewis Redner. Words by Phillips Brooks

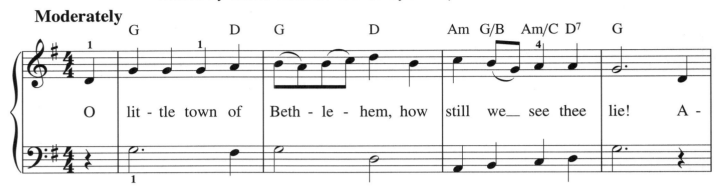

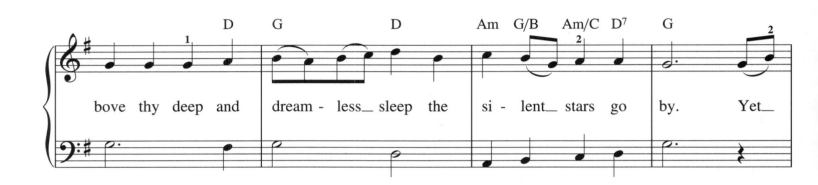

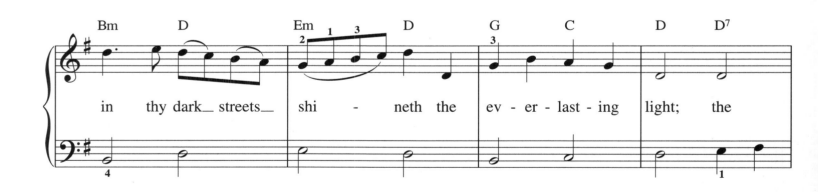

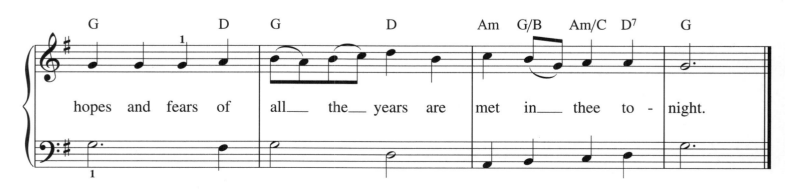

Once In Royal David's City

Music by Henry Gauntlett. Words by Cecil Alexander

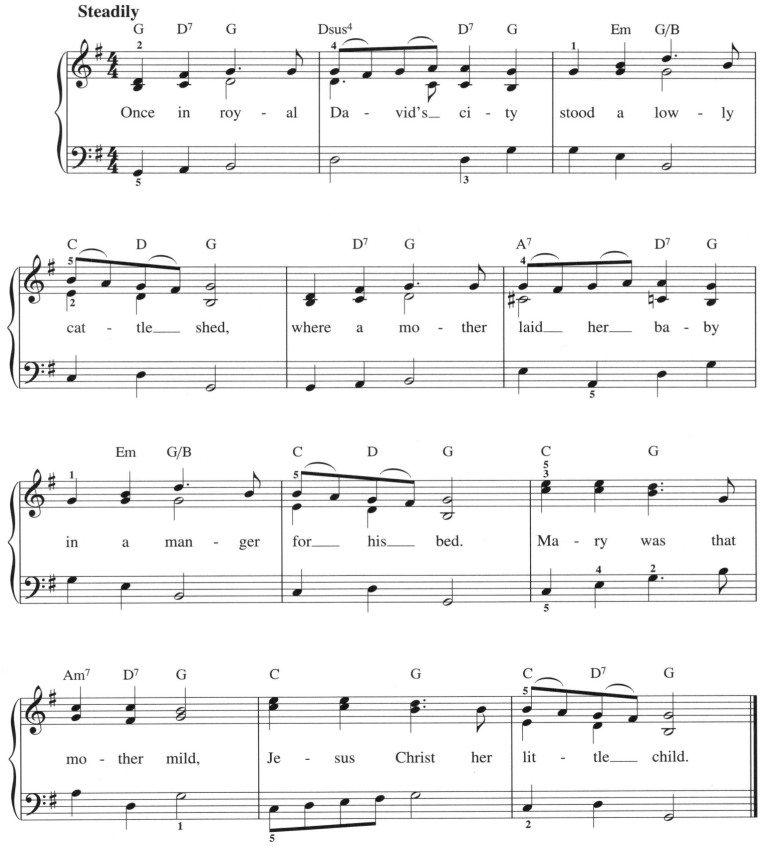

Past Three O'Clock

Music by George Woodward. Words: Traditional

See Amid The Winter's Snow

Music by John Goss. Words by Edward Caswall

Gently, not too fast

See a - mid the win - ter's snow, born for us on earth be - low.

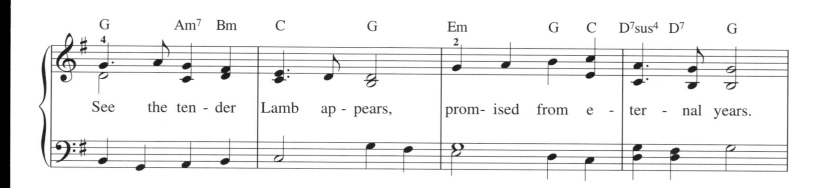

See the ten - der Lamb ap - pears, prom - ised from e - ter - nal years.

Hail, thou ev - er bless - ed morn; hail, re - demp - tion's hap - py dawn!

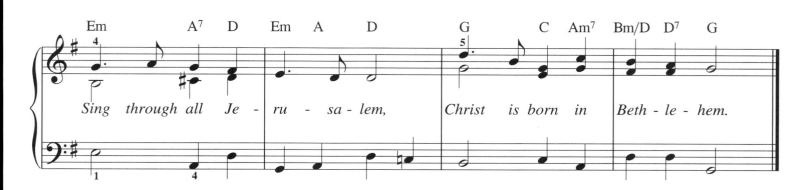

Sing through all Je - ru - sa - lem, Christ is born in Beth - le - hem.

Silent Night

Music by Franz Grüber. Words by Joseph Mohr

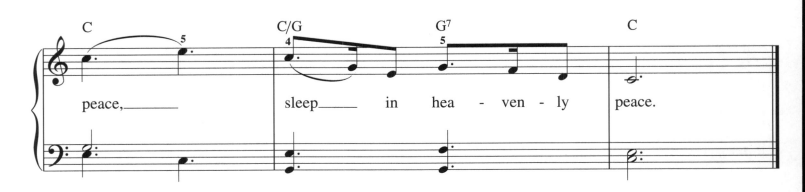

We Three Kings Of Orient Are

Words & Music by John Henry Hopkins

Smooth and flowing

I Saw Three Ships

Traditional

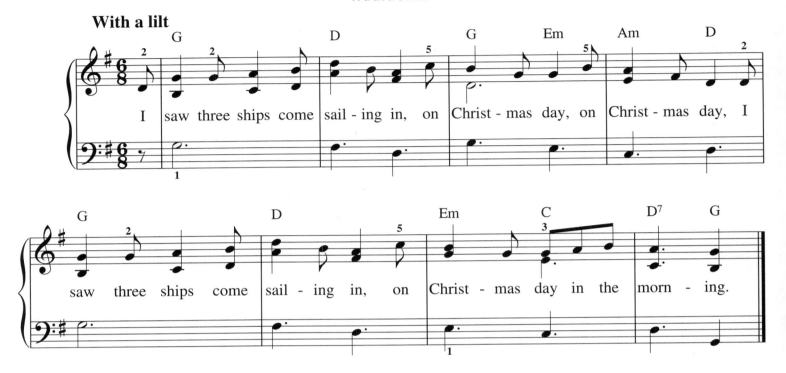

While Shepherds Watched

Music: Traditional. Words by Nahum Tate

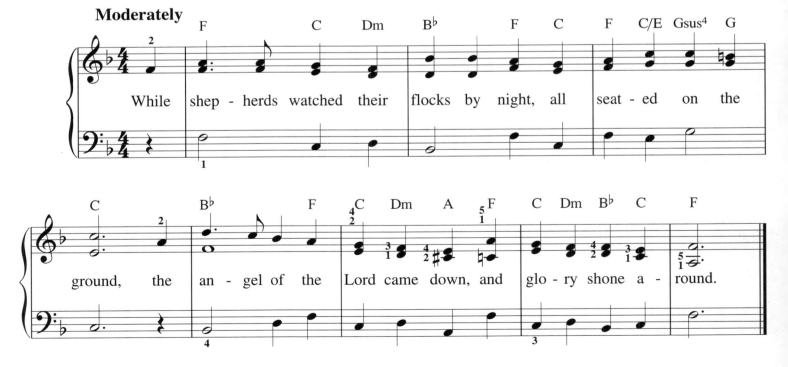

10/06 (60138)